PIANO TOWN
Level 1 • Lessons
By Keith Snell & Diane Hidy

ISBN 0-8497-7325-3

Contents

Waking Up

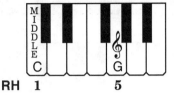

This piece uses only (circle one):

    Treble clef   Bass clef

How many measures are there? _____

How many beats are in each measure? _____

Which measures have half notes? _____ and _____

How many quarter notes will you play? _____

Lunchbox

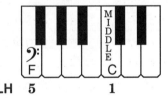

This piece uses only:

    Treble clef   Bass clef

Which measure has quarter notes? _____

Duet for *Waking Up*

Duet for *Lunchbox*

The Backpack

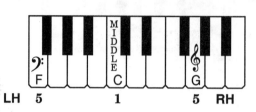

This piece uses the:

Treble staff only   Bass staff only   Grand staff

How many measures are there? ____

How many beats are in each measure? _____

How many dotted half notes are there? ____

Write in the counts. (The first measure is done for you.)

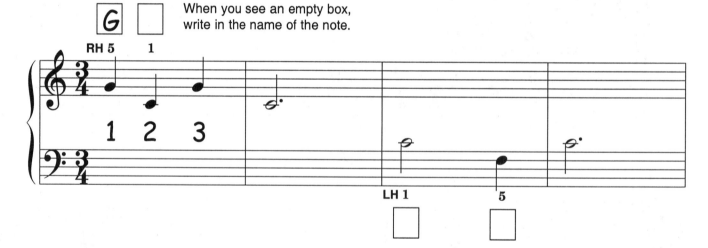

When you see an empty box,
write in the name of the note.

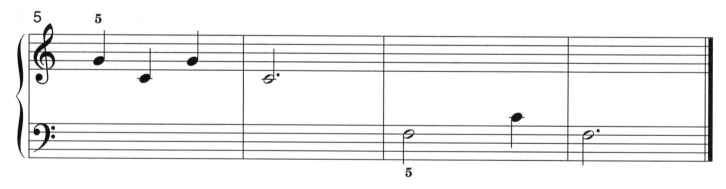

Duet

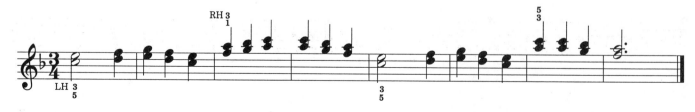

4   MP101

Waiting for the Bus

How many beats are in each measure? _____

How many quarter rests are there? _____

Which measure has the only:

    Half rest? _____

    Whole note? _____

Write in the counts.

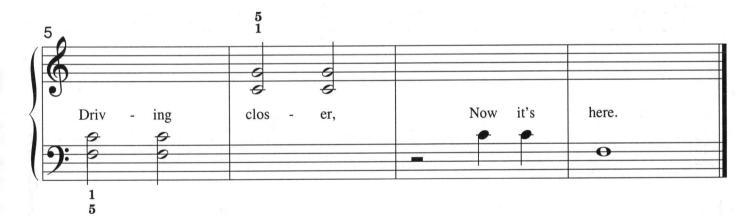

Duet

My New Class

Middle C Position

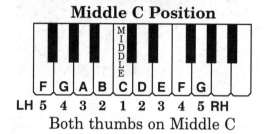

Both thumbs on Middle C

How many measures have 2nds going:

Up? _____

Down? _____

Find and circle the only quarter rest.

How many whole rests are in this piece? _____

Duet (Student plays one octave higher.)

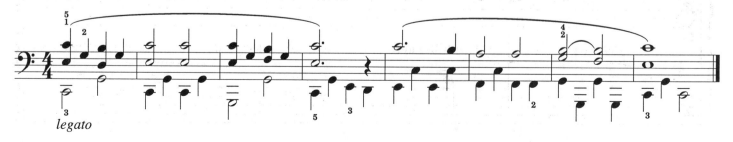

legato

6

New Friends

This piece is: loud   soft

How many measures have:

    3rds on lines? _____

    3rds in spaces? _____

Which measure has half rests?   3   4

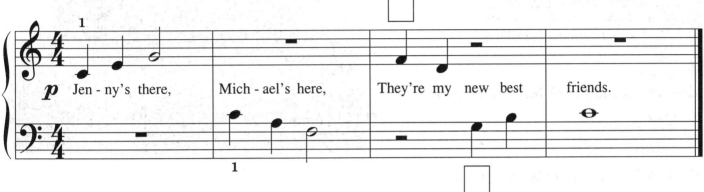

The Globe

This piece is: loud   soft

Which two measures have 4ths?

    1 and 5   2 and 8

How many slurs are in this piece? _____

A slur means to play: legato   staccato

Glitter Glue

Write in the counts.

Which measure has
2nds and a 3rd?   2   3

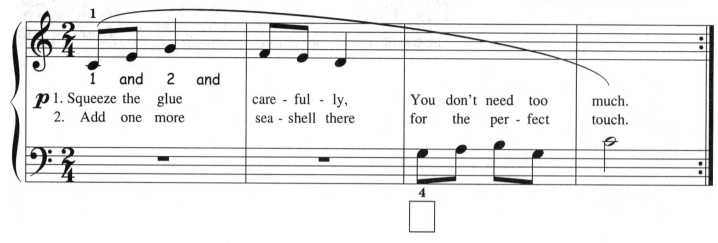

1 and 2 and			
p 1. Squeeze the glue	care - ful - ly,	You don't need too	much.
2. Add one more	sea - shell there	for the per - fect	touch.

4

The Snowflake

Which measure has only 2nds?   5   7

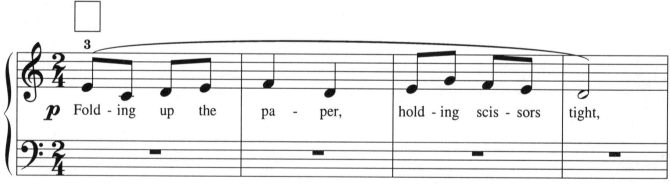

p Fold - ing up the	pa - per,	hold - ing scis - sors	tight,

Snip - ping out a	snow - flake,	beau - ti - ful and	white.

MP101

Skipping Stones

Which measure has only:

   3rds   1   2

   Repeated notes?   3   4

This piece is: legato   staccato

5

1. Skip - ping   a   stone on the   lake is like   wiz - ard - ry.
2. Once it's be - gun   it skips   on   al - most   end - less - ly.

4

Sitting Still

Measures 1 and 2 are
exactly like measures _____ and _____.

All of the measures have
repeated notes, except measures _____ and _____.

1

When I wait for   some-thing good,   I can't sit still   as   I should.

2

5

Hop - ping on my   right foot, then   right to left and   back a - gain.

The Fawn

C Major Five-Finger Position

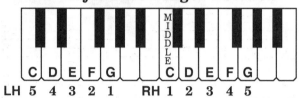

How many times will you play G with your:

RH? _____

LH? _____

In the ear-ly morn-ing at the break of dawn,

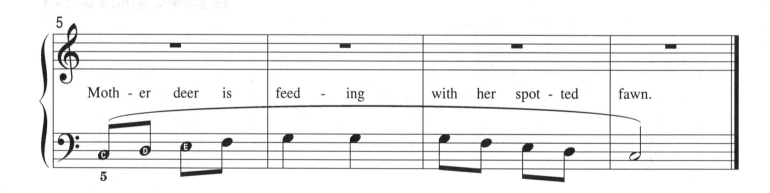

Moth-er deer is feed-ing with her spot-ted fawn.

Duet (Student plays one octave higher.)

10

Owls and Bats

Which measure has only 2nds?   2   3

Our Neighborhood Raccoon

Which measure has only:

4ths?   4   8

5ths?   4   8

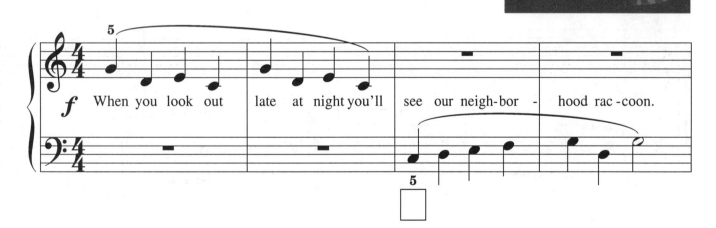

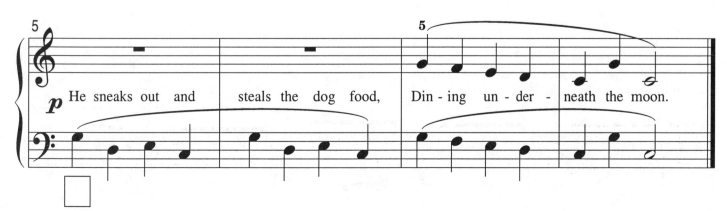

In ancient Rome, they used letters to represent numbers.

I	II	III	IV	V	VI	VII	VIII	IX	X
1	2	3	4	5	6	7	8	9	10

In music, Roman numerals are used to identify chords.

Fanfare in C

In a five-finger position,
you can make two **chords**.

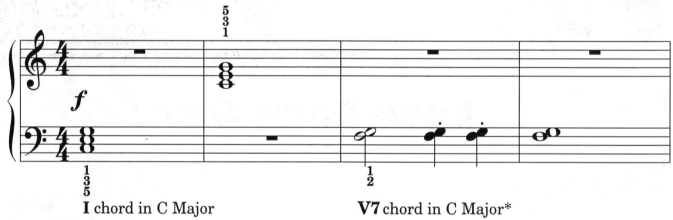

I chord in C Major   **V7** chord in C Major*

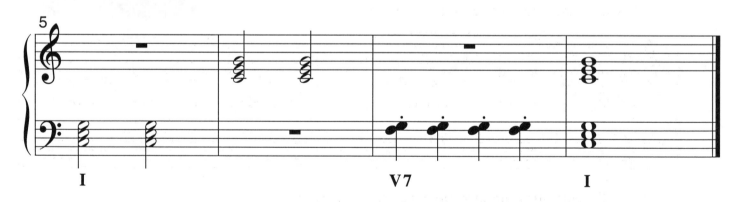

I   V7   I

Duet

LH 3   2   2   2 4   2

* The two notes used to represent the V7 chord
  are an abbreviation of this four-note chord:

Love Each Day

Measures 1 and 2 are
exactly like measures _____ and ____.

Folk Melody
"Love Somebody"

Melody: the part of the music you sing.

Chords often **accompany** (go with) a melody.

mezzo forte: medium loud

Turning Cartwheels

In this piece, the melody is:

    Legato   Staccato

The accompaniment is:

    Legato   Staccato

How many beats will you hold the
tied notes in the last two measures? _____

Play the accompaniment
softer than the melody.

14

Feeling Sneaky

What black key will you play in:

Measure 1 and 2? _____

Measure 9 and 10? _____

How many times will you play:

E♭ in measure 3? _____

F♯ in measure 11? _____

mf When I'm feel-ing sneak-y care-ful you should be, *p*

Still E♭

A flat lasts
the whole measure.

I'll creep up be-hind you, when you turn I'll flee. *p*

p In my mask you can't tell *f* that it's me!

Still F♯

A sharp lasts
the whole measure.

mf I'll creep up be-hind you, when you turn I'll flee. *p*

Dinosaur Museum

How many times will you
play B♭ in measure 1? _____

Dinosaur Museum is in the
Key of F Major: it uses B♭ instead of B.

Another way to change every B to B♭ is to write
a flat sign on the B line at the beginning of each staff.
This is the F Major **key signature**.

Dinosaur Museum 2

16

Dinosaur Tracking

Dinosaur Tracking is in the key of _____ Major.

Which hand will play B♭? **LH   RH**

Which finger will you use? 5 4 3 2 1

This piece has 3 **lines** of music.
There are 4 measures in each line.

Line 1 is exactly like line: 2   3

mf Pull my pack up / on my back, / Hope I find a / gi - ant track.

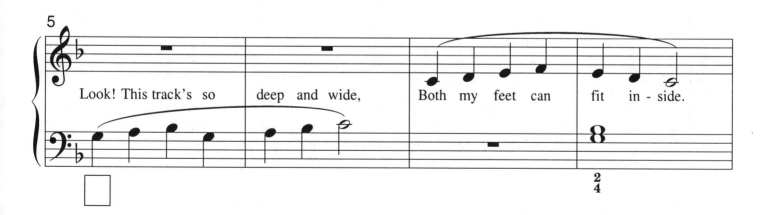

Look! This track's so / deep and wide, / Both my feet can / fit in - side.

Now I know they / once walked here, / In a pre - his - tor - ic year.

The Stegosaurus

F Major Five-Finger Position

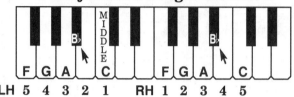

Circle the finger that will play B♭ in each hand.

LH 5 4 3 2 1   **RH** 1 2 3 4 5

Which measures have 3rds? _____ and _____

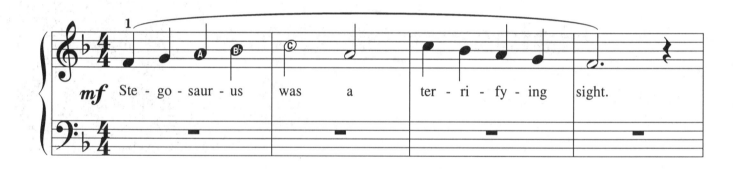

Ste - go - saur - us   was   a   ter - ri - fy - ing   sight.

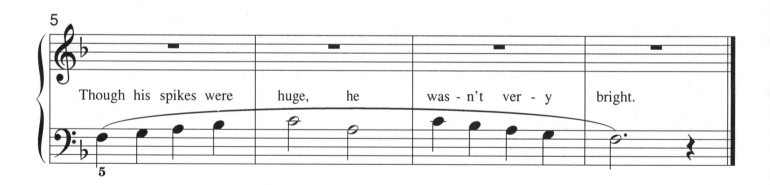

Though his spikes were   huge,   he   was - n't ver - y   bright.

Duet (Student plays one octave higher.)

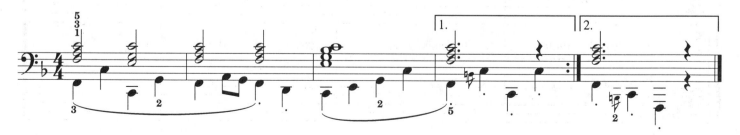

The Seismosaurus

How many measures have:

3rds? _____

Eighth notes? _____

Seis - mo - saur - us was the big - gest one. If you saw him, you had bet - ter run.

Maiasaur Mothers

Which measures have:

Staccato notes? _____ and _____

3rds? _____ and _____

Mai - a - saur moth - ers were tru - ly the best,

mezzo piano: medium soft

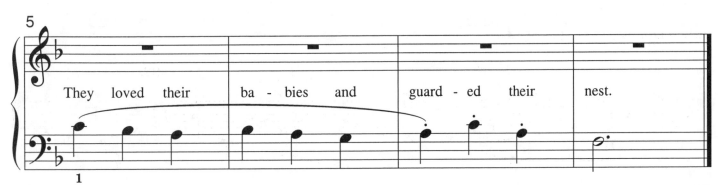

They loved their ba - bies and guard - ed their nest.

Fanfare in F

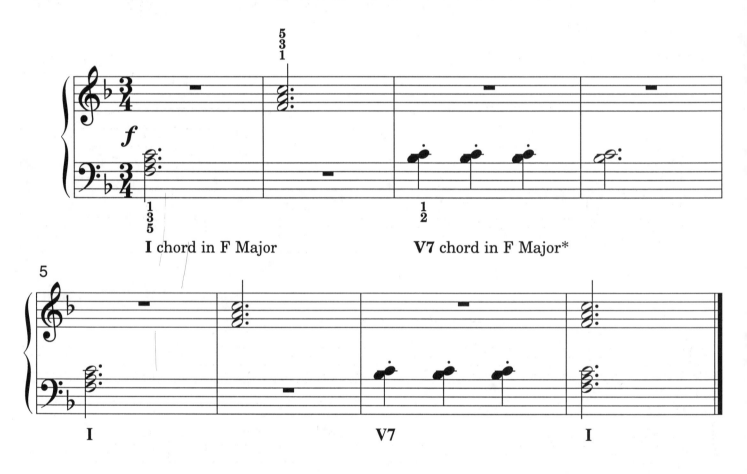

I chord in F Major   V7 chord in F Major*

I   V7   I

Duet

LH 5

* Abbreviation of:

20

MP101

Dinosaur Mystery

How many times will you play V7? _____

Which measure has the only A♭? _____

Folk Melody
"Go Tell Aunt Rhodie"

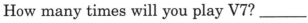

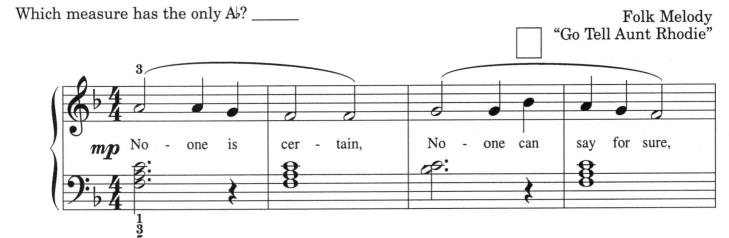

No - one is cer - tain, No - one can say for sure,

No - bod - y knows why the di - no - saurs are gone.

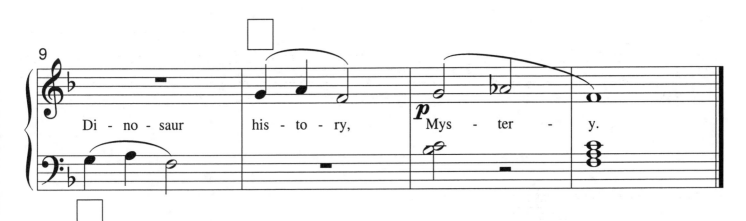

Di - no - saur his - to - ry, Mys - ter - y.

Children's Garden

Position for RH

RH 1 2 3 4 5

How many times will
you play F♯ in measure 3? _____

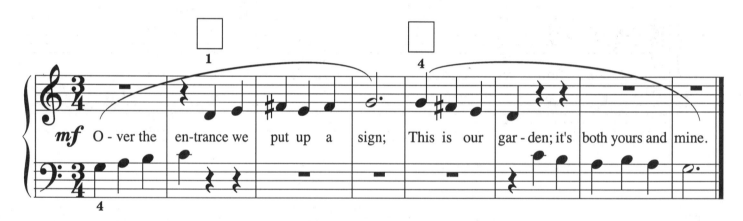

Children's Garden is in the
Key of G Major: it uses F♯ instead of F.

Another way to change every F to F♯ is to write
a sharp sign on the F line at the beginning of each staff.
This is the G Major **key signature**.

Children's Garden 2

MP101

Sunflowers

Sunflowers is in the key of _____ Major.

Which hand will play F♯? **LH** **RH**

Which finger will you use? 1 2 3 4 5

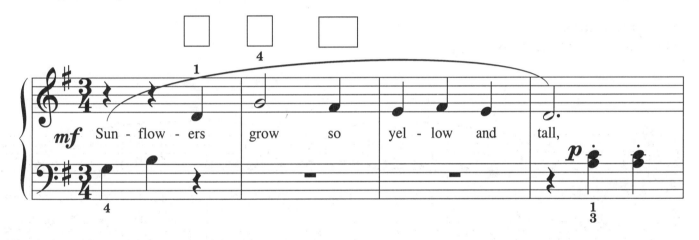

mf Sun - flow - ers   grow   so   yel - low   and   tall,

p

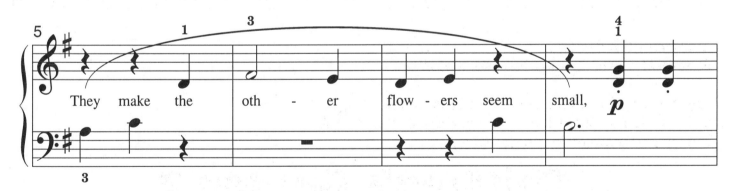

They   make   the   oth - er   flow - ers   seem   small,

p

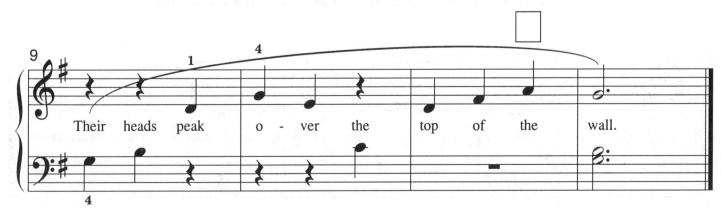

Their   heads   peak   o - ver   the   top   of   the   wall.

Cabbage Lunch

G Major Five-Finger Position

How many times will you play D with your:

LH? _____

RH? _____

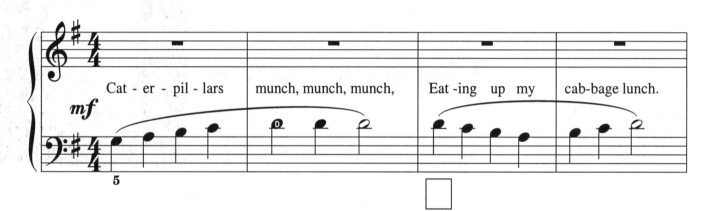

Cat - er - pil - lars | munch, munch, munch, | Eat -ing up my | cab-bage lunch.

I'll be nice and | let them stay, | Don't like cab - bage | an - y - way!

Duet (Student plays one octave higher.)

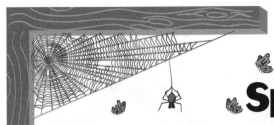

Diminuendo ⟩

Spider Webs

Which measure has 5ths?   3   4

Practice hands separately first.

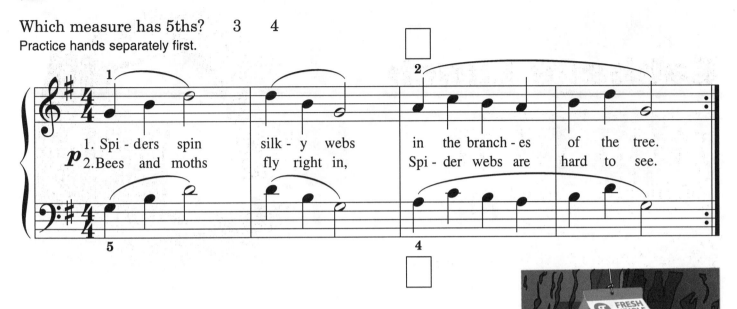

The Bird Feeder

Measures 3 and 7 are:

the same   different

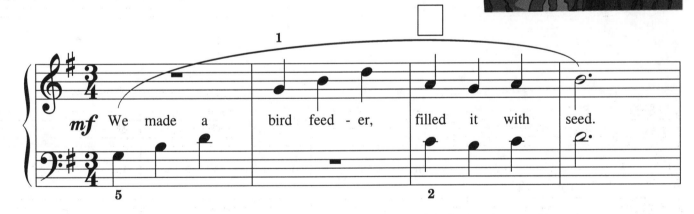

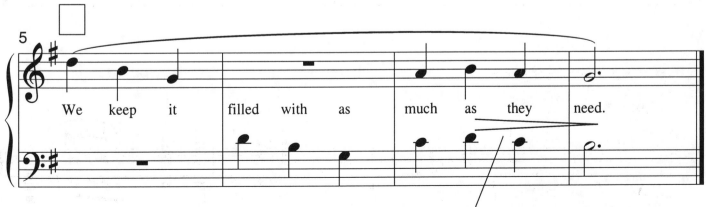

This sign means **diminuendo**: gradually softer.

Fanfare in G

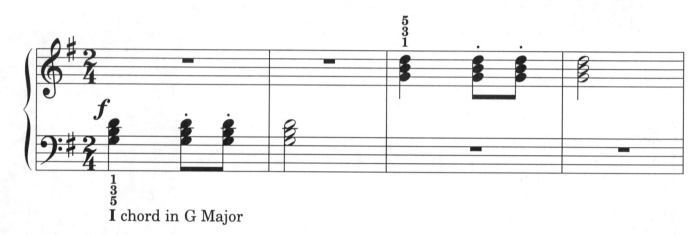

I chord in G Major

V7 chord in G Major*   **I**

Duet

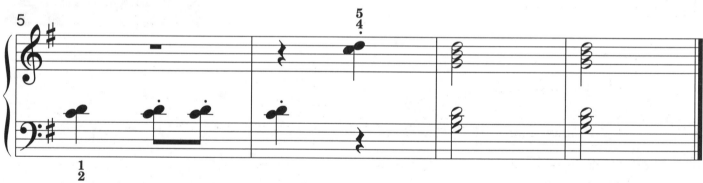

* Abbreviation of:

MP101

In the Spring

Line 2 is exactly like line: 3   4

The **LH** is tied from measure 7 to 8.
The **LH** is tied *again* from measure _____ to _____.

crescendo

Folk Melody
"Lightly Row"

mf In the spring,   song-birds sing,   *p* time to do some   *mf* gar-den-ing.

This sign means **crescendo**: gradually louder.

Pull the weeds,   plant the seeds,   wa - ter them each   day.

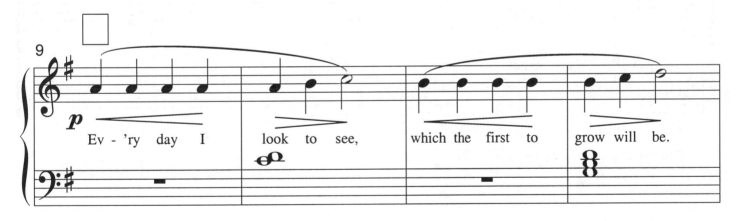

p Ev - 'ry day I   look to see,   which the first to   grow will be.

mf Pull the weeds,   plant the seeds,   watch the flow - ers   bloom.

MP101

27

The Hayride

G Major Five-Finger Position with the LH Lower

LH 5 4 3 2 1   RH 1 2 3 4 5

Play and name these notes aloud.

f Sit - ting in the | wag - on it's a | might - y bump - y | ride.

The County Fair

Which hand has the melody?   **LH   RH**

Which measure has the only 4th?   6   7

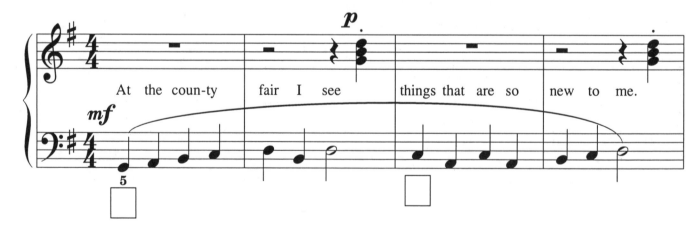

mf   At the coun-ty | fair I see | things that are so | new to me.

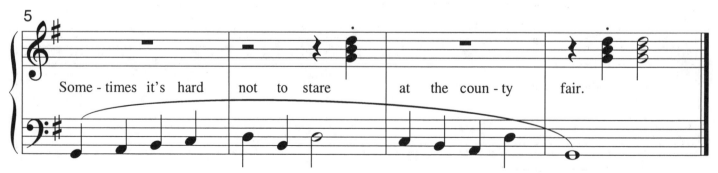

Some - times it's hard | not to stare | at the coun - ty | fair.

The Highland Fling

Line 1 is exactly like line: 2   3   4

The **LH** in measure 1 and 2 is:

      slurred   tied

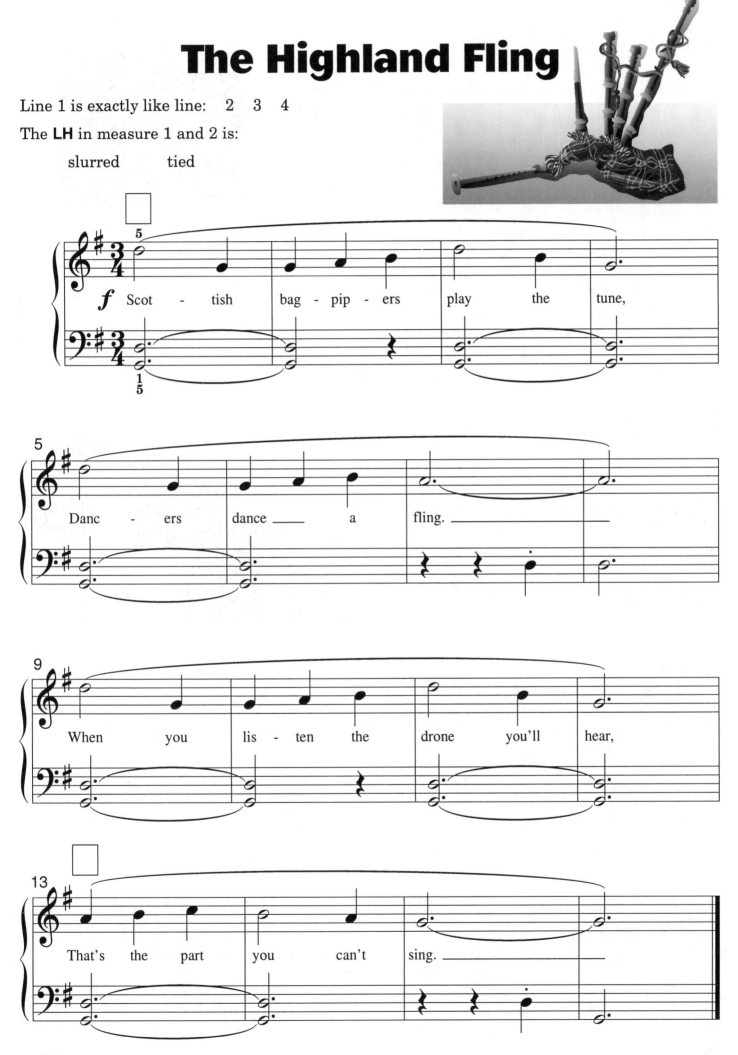

Scot - tish bag - pip - ers play the tune,

Danc - ers dance ___ a fling. ___

When you lis - ten the drone you'll hear,

That's the part you can't sing. ___

Baseball Cap

Baseball Cap uses the notes of
the C Major five-finger position.

Wear - ing my new | base - ball cap, | Make three dou - ble | plays.
E - ven when I | go to sleep, | On my head it | stays.

Here is *Baseball Cap* again. This time,
it is in the G Major five-finger position.

Baseball Cap

Wear - ing my new | base - ball cap, | Make three dou - ble | plays.
E - ven when I | go to sleep, | On my head it | stays.

Now, move your hands to
the F Major five-finger position.
Play *Baseball Cap* one more time.
(Remember to play B♭.)

You have played *Baseball Cap*
in three different keys!
This is called **transposing**.

My Best Jeans

Key of _____ Major

My best jeans fit on - ly me, There's a hole just for my knee.
E - ven though they're worn and old, They're worth more to me than gold.

Transpose to F Major,
then to G Major.

Hat and Gloves

Key of _____ Major

Snow - y winds blow cold out - side, In my gloves my fin - gers hide.
Hat pulled o - ver my cold ears, It's the cold - est day in years!

Transpose to C Major,
then to G Major.

My Favorite Shoes

Key of _____ Major

My fav - 'rite shoes fit me be - fore.
It makes me sad, They fit no more.

Transpose to F Major,
then to C Major.

Time to Get Up

The pieces you have played until now
started on beat one of the first measure.
A piece of music can actually start on
any beat the composer chooses.

Time to Get Up starts on beat four.
To understand why, look at the last measure.
It only has three beats.
The missing fourth beat,
or **upbeat**, starts this piece.

Key of _____ Major.

American Bugle Call

It's time to get up, it's time to get up, it's time to get up this morn-ing. Just

slide out of bed, don't land on your head, it's time to get up right now!

Transpose to C Major,
then to G Major.

MP101

When the Saints Go Marching In

How many beats should there be in each measure? _____

How many beats are in the last measure? _____

Circle the beats that are missing from the last measure: 1   2   3   4

The missing beats are in the first measure. On which beat does it begin? _____

Key of _____ Major.

African-American Spiritual

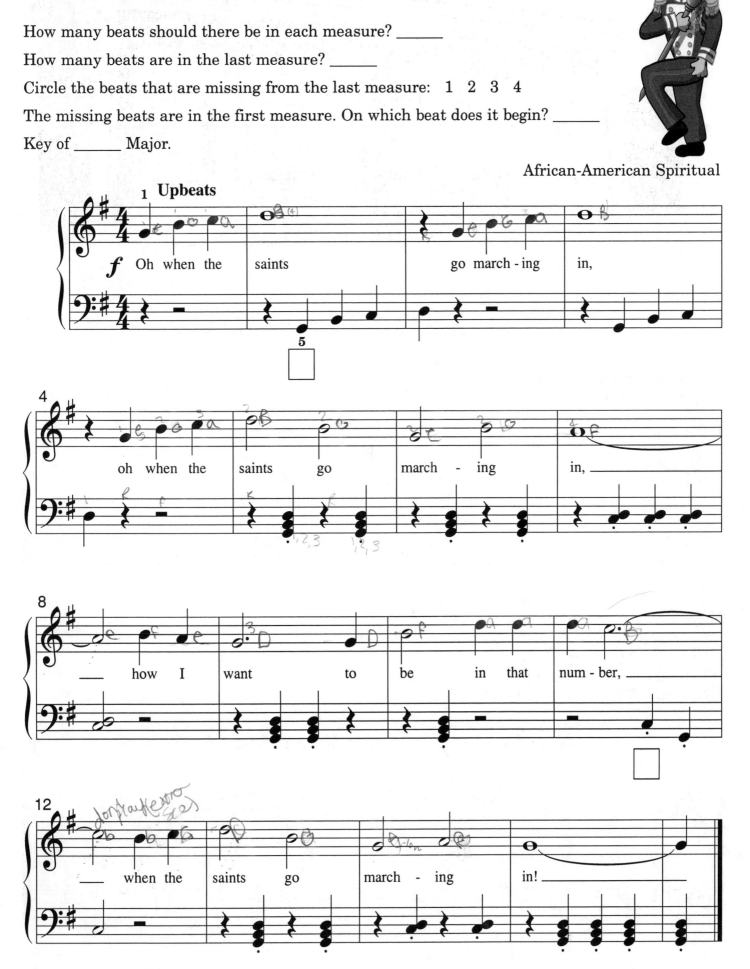

Simple Gifts

How many beats should there be in each measure? _____

How many beats are in the last measure? _____

Circle the beats that are missing from the last measure: 1   2   3   4

The missing beats are in the first measure. On which beat does it begin? _____

American Hymn Tune

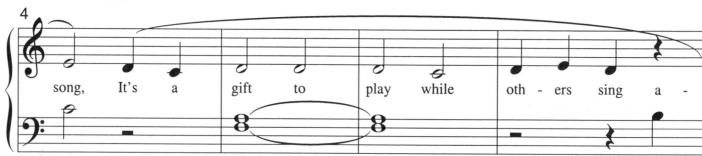

ritardando: gradually slower.

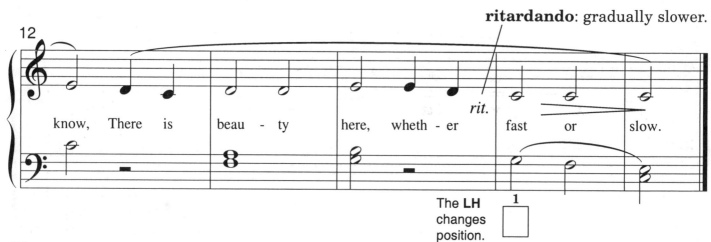

34

MP101

Candlelight

How many beats should be in each measure? _____

On which beat does this piece begin? 1 2 3

How many times will your left hand play a broken C chord? _____

D. C. al Fine

da capo al fine:
go back to the beginning
and play to the *Fine* (end).

Fanfare

The letters above the staff
name each new chord.

Move your hand
to the new position
during the rest.

Square Dance

Each measure uses the notes of only one chord (C, F or G).
Write the chord names in the boxes.

MP101

Dance With Me

Write the chord names in the boxes.

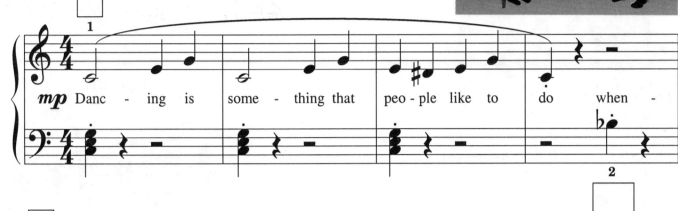

mp Danc - ing is some - thing that peo - ple like to do when -

5

mf ev - er they're hap - py and some - one else is too. They

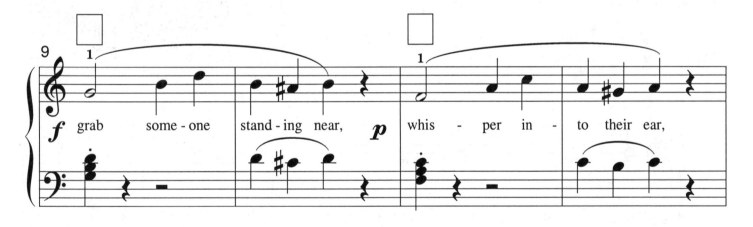

9

f grab some - one stand - ing near, *p* whis - per in - to their ear,

13

"Let's take a chance and kick off our shoes and dance."

f

Low C

The pedal on the right is called the **damper pedal**.
When you hold it down, the dampers lift off the strings.
With the pedal down, notes continue to sound
even when you let go of the keys.

Town Hall

The pedal should be held down
for the entire piece.

True   False

In which measure does
your **LH** move down? _____

Key of _____ Major.

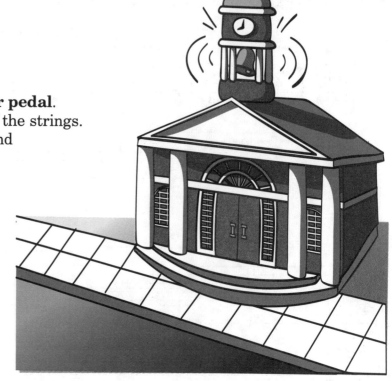

Westminster Chimes

Push the pedal down.   Keep the pedal down.

Let the pedal up.

It sounds best when the pedal and keys
come up at the same time.

MP101

The Lighthouse

Which line of music has pedal signs
that last only two measures? 1 2 3 4

Which line uses two hand positions? 1 2 3 4

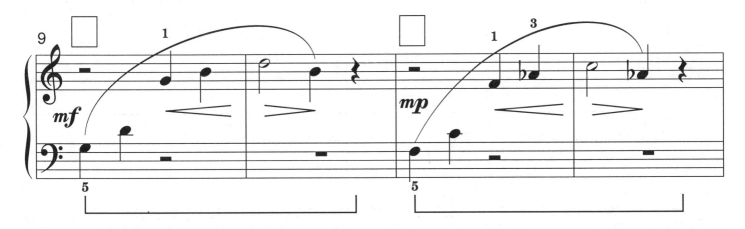

LH cross over

The Cookie Jar

Your right hand should play one octave higher
from measure 9 to the end of the piece.

True   False

Key of _____ Major.

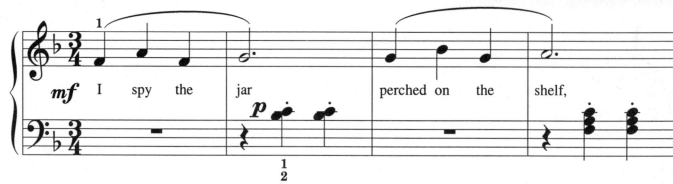

mf I spy the jar   perched on the shelf,

Move your **RH** up
during the rest.

I want to reach it all by my - self.

When the **8va** sign is *above* notes,
play one octave (eight notes) higher.

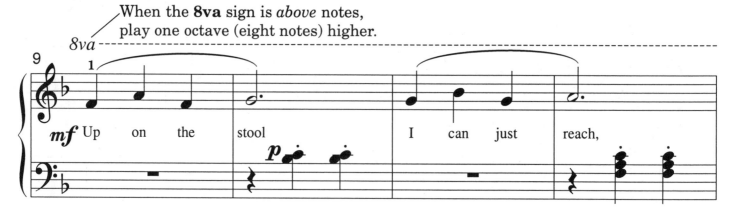

mf Up on the stool   I can just reach,

Oat - meal and fudge, I'll have one *rit.* of each.

Transpose to C Major,
then to G Major.

MP101

The Flashlight

The **LH** plays one octave lower at the end of line 2.

The **LH** plays one octave lower *again* at the end of line _____.

Practice the **LH** alone first.

mf When I wake up in the dark-ness scar-y sights ap-pear,

Move your **LH** during the rest.

I feel brav-er when I simp-ly keep my flash-light near.

8va

When the **8va** sign is *under* notes, play one octave lower.

f Flip the switch the light comes on, Ev-'ry thing is clear!

mf When I flip my flash-light on the shad-ows dis-ap-pear. p

8va

MP101

Driving Lessons

In the melody, how many times will your:

RH play E natural? _____

LH play F natural? _____

Natural: cancels a flat or sharp.
A note with a natural sign
is always a white key.

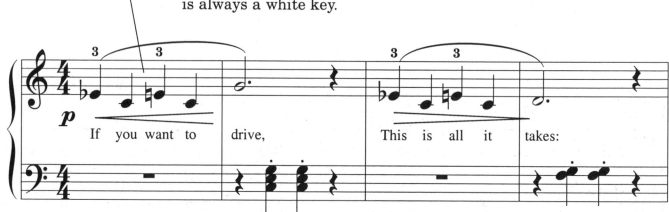

p

If you want to drive,   This is all it takes:

First you press the gas,   Then put on the brakes.

42

Bumper Cars

Almost every measure
starts with a black key.

Which two measures
start on a white key?

9 and 10   11 and 12

Key of _____ Major

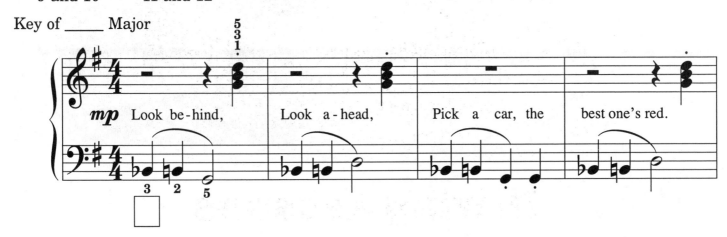

Look be-hind,   Look a - head,   Pick a car, the   best one's red.

Slide in - side,   Buck - le up,   Take the red car   for a spin.

Bump - er cars are   made to bump,   Bump - er cars are   made to thump.

Accent: play the note
(or notes) louder.

Nev - er lasts quite   long e - nough,   Bump - er   cars!

The Valentine

Write in the counts.

The 3rd line of music
has repeated notes and:

4ths   5ths

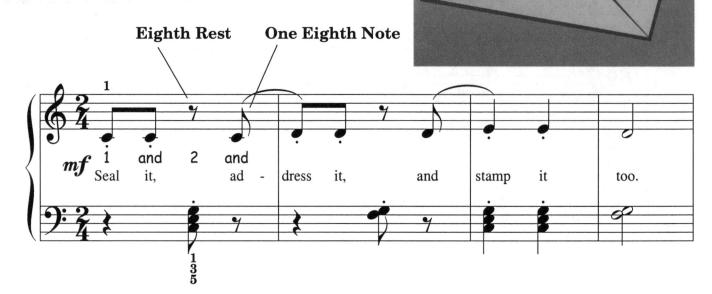

Eighth Rest   One Eighth Note

1 and 2 and
Seal it, ad - dress it, and stamp it too.

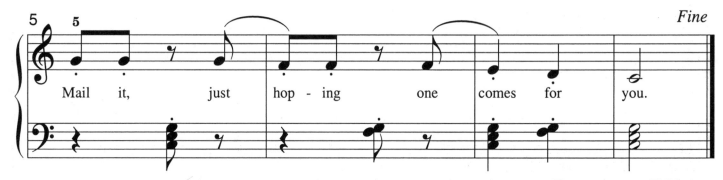

Fine

Mail it, just hop - ing one comes for you.

Transpose to F Major,
then to G Major.

D.C. al Fine

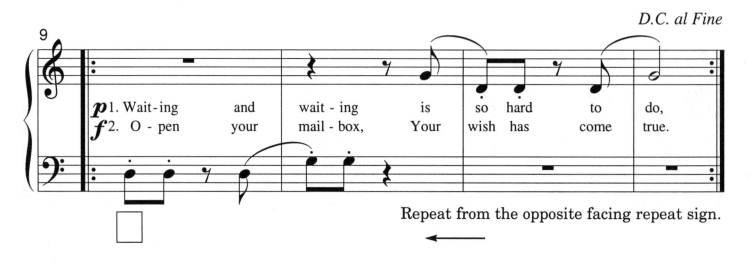

1. Wait-ing and wait - ing is so hard to do,
2. O - pen your mail - box, Your wish has come true.

Repeat from the opposite facing repeat sign.

P.S.

Write in the counts.
(Measures 1 and 5 are done for you.)

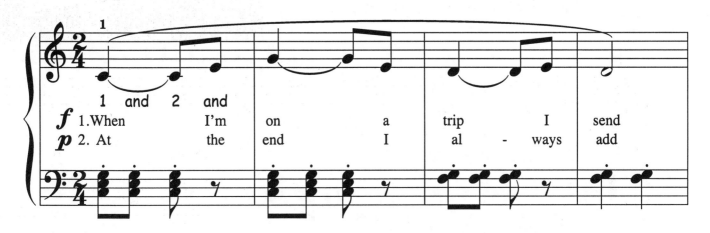

f 1.When I'm on a trip I send
p 2. At the end I al - ways add

1 and 2 and

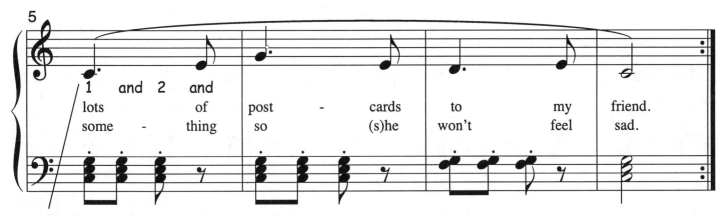

1 and 2 and
lots of post - cards to my friend.
some - thing so (s)he won't feel sad.

Dotted quarter note: same as a quarter note
tied to an eighth note.

Coda (an added ending)

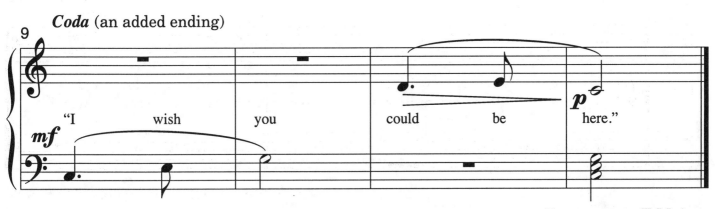

mf "I wish you could be here."

Transpose to F Major,
then to G Major.

Alouette

In which measure
does your **LH** move down? _____

The notes in measures 7 and 8 are all:

    B's   D's

Key of _____ Major

French Folk Tune

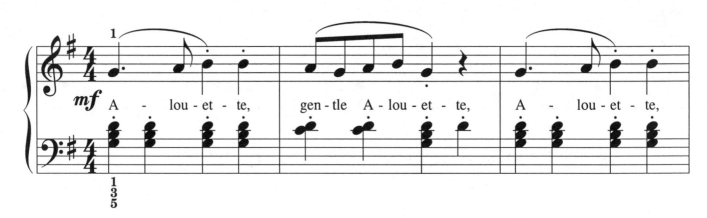

46   MP101

Certificate of Achievement

This certifies that

_____

has successfully completed

Piano Town Lessons, Level One

and is promoted to Level Two.

Teacher _____

Date _____